UNCLE ZEKIE SEH:
Tales of Old Jamaica

June 1, 2021

Sybil Leslie

Sybil Leslie
North Carolina, USA

ISBN 979-8404958980

Printed in United States of America

CONTENTS

Introduction

Food and Dining Traditions

Household Chores

Self-Care

Church

Having Fun

Celebrations

Folklore

About the Author

Sybil Leslie is a retired teacher, who is a historian, storyteller and published author. Her passion is the retention and spread of Jamaican culture. She was born in Bethel Town, Westmoreland, and received her early education there, at Bethlehem Teachers College, as well as at the University of the West Indies (UWI), Mona, where she received an M.A. in Educational Administration and at UWI Cave Hill, where she received, an M. Phil in History.

She taught at different levels of the Jamaican education system, including Shortwood Teachers College, where she was head of the Social Studies Department, and UWI Cave Hill.

Sybil has published previous works, namely a series of four Social Studies text books for schools in Jamaica: *The Caribbean: Our Land and People; The Caribbean: Our Changing Environment; The Caribbean and the Wider World; and Our Caribbean Neighbors.*

Since her retirement, she has been committed to sharing Jamaican culture with American audiences. She migrated to the U.S. in 1993 and until 2015, she played a key role in the Atlanta Jamaica Association, serving for many years as head of the Education and Family Relations Committees. In 2010, she formed a Jamaican folk singing group, the Sugar Canes, which still exists today and has performed at a variety of functions, both in and out of the State of Georgia.

Sybil has received several prestigious honors and awards for her work as a "cultural ambassador". These include: National honors (the Badge of Honor) from the Government of Jamaica for her contribution to the promotion of Jamaican culture in the U.S.; the UJOIA plaque in recognition of her continuous support of the Jamaican community in Atlanta; the President's award from NAJASO; an award from the Atlanta Jamaica Association for her work in promoting Jamaican culture; and Diaspora Honors from the Consul-General of Jamaica in Miami, for her contribution in commemorating Jamaica's 50th Anniversary of Independence.

She was married to Astley Noel Leslie (now deceased), who held senior positions in the Jamaican Government as well as the International Labor Organization, and who served several terms as President of the Atlanta Jamaica Association. She has two daughters, Winsome Leslie, Ph.D. and Heather Leslie-Brown, M.D., FACOG, as well as two granddaughters, Noelle and Natalie. She currently lives in Charlotte, North Carolina.

INTRODUCTION

Uncle Zekie is a fictitious character. He is representing me and telling stories about the things that I remember from my childhood in Jamaica. He is a well-educated man and was born long ago in the early part of the twentieth century. These are real and true stories, that are part of the foundation of Jamaican culture.

The aim of these stories is to encourage us to think about the past, our rich heritage and the important and humble beginnings that contributed to our culture. They describe some of the traditions which began after the Emancipation, that is, the end of slavery, when those who were former slaves (enslaved persons) were suddenly thrown into free villages. The villagers had to do their best with what they had, a modest and humble existence, while the rich folk – e.g. landowners - lived in luxury. Even though these former enslaved persons did not have much, they were self-reliant and knew how to enjoy life, in spite of circumstances.

Younger readers will learn about how their ancestors in Jamaica lived, and it will remind the older folk, who already know about these things, but in the busy hum of today's world, they might have forgotten. I have been inspired to record these stories for your enjoyment.

Pleasant Reading!

Sybil Leslie
July 2021

To each of my readers I say:

You are the chocolate in mi chocolate tea
The goat's milk in mi coffee
The ackee in mi salt fish
The pigs tail in mi stew peas
The flour in mi dumplin
The parch corn in mi asham
The green banana in mi duckanoo
The coconut milk in mi rice an peas
The mackerel in mi run dung

You are an angel indeed!

FOOD & DINING TRADITIONS

ONE

The Market

There is a market in every community in Jamaica. It usually is a large building with many stalls where people go and sell their wares, and also food items. It is convenient, because so many necessary items are sold in one place.

Uncle Zekie seh that one time he took his friend on a tour of the local market. First, he went to the meat stall. The butcher was there with his cutting board. He was dressed in a white apron, with a turban or cap on his head, and he had his machete and knife. There were different kinds of meat --beef, pork, mutton, liver, cow foot, and cow tail, which we now call "oxtail". The meat was just pretty hanging there, and people were in line to make purchases. There were different parts of meat for different occasions --for stew, roast -- and soup bones. The meat was cheap --not as expensive as today.

Then there was a stall with underwear for both men and women, and a sign saying: "Buy yuh underwear here an look sexy." There were panties, stockings, brazzieres and girdles for women; underpants and merinos for men. The vendor was shouting: "Buy dem an look pretty dung dere." Then Uncle seh: "A who gwine see dem?" The answer was: "Neva yuh mind."

Soon they came to a food stall – yellow yam, white yam, all kind a yam, dasheen, coco, breadfruit, green banana. The vendor look on Zekie and him friend, and say: "Oonu nah buy nutting? Galang wid you mawga foot woman, yuh knock knee an yuh hungry belly."

At the fruit stall there was star apple, mango, paw paw, guava, apple, soursop, jew plum, sweet and sour orange to name a few, and also juices like star apple mixed with condensed milk, soursop juice, jew plum drink, and ice cream. The vendor says: "Come on pretty lady, yuh so fat and yuh look tired. Refresh yuh body wid some a these nice drinks. Dem wi mek yuh feel good."

Then there was a woman sitting with her two feet close together, and her knees far apart and a big tread bag in her lap. She say: "Just one shilling, an a can read yuh han and tell yuh bout yuh past and yuh future. Siddung ya so an open yuh two han and show mi de palm. Then she said to Uncle Zekie's friend: "Hear dis now. You did married an divorce, an now yuh living wid another man. You know seh you pregnant, in de early stage? No badda fi try hold awn pan dis man, for him married an him wife deh a yard."

Soon they moved to a stall, where the vendor was wearing a red head wrap, a long wide, red flaired skirt, and a black blouse. She held up a sign: 'Come Here For Healing.' She swear that she is a Christian and that the Lord put her on this earth and command her to come to the market to heal people, so she is obedient to the Lord. She had soursop leaf to help you sleep and to stop you from wetting you bed; cerasee to cleanse the blood and keep you skin clean; ginger root and mint to make tea to settle your stomach; leaf of life for colds; pimento leaf and mango leaf for stomach ache; chew stick for cleaning your teeth.[1]

This lady have so much bush for the body around her, that you can hardly see her, and the people just buying every minute. Uncle Zekie seh that at that point him tired and him think that him show the lady enough. So, he took her over to the stall where they were selling food: peg bread, hard dough bread, cake, pudding, fry fish, fry dumpling, bulla and pear, stew beef, ackee and saltfish, and much more. They relax there and have a good meal.

But Uncle Zekie is not so young, so he would know all about these things. Such was life in the old days.

---

[1] Chew stick is a vine growing wild in the bush. Cut a piece, wash it and keep chewing it, and it cleans your teeth like a tooth brush.

TWO

The Kitchen

Uncle Zekie seh that people have to eat, that "food is de staff of life" and "yuh are what yuh eat." So, a place to cook is a necessity. One time, he told me about the kitchen they used to have in the old days.

Long ago, the kitchen was a little building that they built not too far from the main house. It had to be close, because you have to carry the food from there to the house you lived in.

"De kitchen did mek of board an maybe de roof cover wid shingles – small pieces of wood of de same shape an size - nailed down on some pieces of board all over de top, what dem call rafters. De floor was perhaps board or just dirt. De kitchen did have one or two windows so yuh can get some fresh air, and yuh could fall asleep in dere."

He described to me where the cooking took place.

"In de kitchen was a firewall mek out of stones put together wid some mixture to keep dem firm – someting like concrete. De firewall was high enough dat it was easy to stand up an put yuh pot on de fire. On de firewall was three big stones, an on dem, a strong piece of iron, sitting comfortable. Den yuh made de fire wid pieces of wood, put together between de stones, drop some kerosine oil on dem, an light wid a match. Den yuh have yuh fire. De pot was either a Dutch pot, or a big iron pot (three-foot pot) dat yuh can set steady on de fire. Den yuh start cooking.

Sometimes a bench was in de kitchen where yuh could sit down an attend to yuh pot if yuh need to. Some kitchens were divided into two sections. De smaller section was called de butchery. Here yuh can store food -- yams, potatoes, bananas (to ripen or cook), sugar, corned meat, preserves that yuh make – guava jelly, marmalade -- items for baking cakes an puddings. One man did store yam in de butchery til it grow an de stem show out de window!"

According to Uncle Zekie, as time passed on and houses became more stylish and bigger, electricity was then the order of the day for who could afford it. So, the kitchen was now built inside the house with all the trappings -- refrigerator and big stove. So, cooking was now much easier. Some good nice Jamaican food was made in the old time kitchen! No fast food.

But you know, this is part of Jamaican culture, and we can look back and smile when we remember the experiences we had in the Kitchen.

THREE

The Coffee Walk and Making Coffee

Believe me, what I am writing is the real truth. Uncle Zekie tells me stories all the time and I believe him. He is honest and he don't tell lies.

He told me one day about his grandmother's coffee walk. He doesn't know why they call it "Coffee Walk", but all he knows is that there were a number of coffee trees growing together covering a big piece of land. The trees were tall and the branches entwined together with little vines forming a canopy, and you could walk under them – "yuh could tek a good walk." The trees bear coffee and sometimes birds and even rats live among the branches. His brother used to take his slingshot and shoot the birds in the trees.

The ground in the coffee walk was flat and smooth and nice, and his grandmother used to take a coconut broom and sweep it clean. A coconut broom comes from the heart of the coconut tree, from the top between the branches, and it is sturdy, with branches that you can use as a broom. When rat cut the coffee, the berries fall on the ground. Uncle Zekie seh that they call it 'rat cut coffee'. He used to collect the rat cut coffee, process it, and sell it to get money for Christmas. Sometimes he used to spread a mat under the coffee trees and relax and sleep.

---

[2] Catapult

Coffee is really a pod with the coffee bean inside. He seh that when the beans are ripe, they have a purplish color. His grandmother put them in a stone mortar, and beat them gently with a mortar stick to get off the pulp, leaving the beans. Then she wash the beans and put them on a zinc to dry. "De iron pot or dutch pot comes in handy. She parch de seeds on de fire until dey get a brown color. She beat dem in de mortar again and sieve dem to get out de nice brown coffee."

In those days it was different from today. Uncle Zekie tell me that his grandmother had a coffee bag made out of thin cloth with a draw string. She put the ground coffee in there and dipped it into some boiling water in a pot on the fire until it get a nice brown color. Then she squeezed out the bag and hung it in a place over the fire wall, so she could use it another time. Adding milk and sugar, especially condensed milk, was just great.

Uncle Zekie seh that at the time, there was no percolator, or refined coffee sold in the stores. Things gradually were different, but he don't know if it was better. He think that people lost the skill of making coffee the old fashioned way. Even though it took time, it was enjoyable.

FOUR

Making Sugar

Uncle Zekie tell me that "fi mek sugar nuh easy." He seh that one girl at a school concert went up to say a poem, and when the people stared on her, she shout out and say: " If yuh tink it easy, come up yah." So he seh, with a smile, "if yuh tink it easy fi mek sugar, try it nuh."

He told me that his cousin Terry had plenty land, a few acres, and he decided to plant cane in part of it, plenty cane, you know, black cane, white cane, ribbon cane, toad eye, you name it, all kinds of cane. Next, the question is, what he going to do with all this cane? So he got people to build a boiling house and fixed it up with a sugar mill to make sugar.

Let me tell you how he described the boiling house.

"It is a little house wid a roof an everything, but it have a big roller to squeeze out de cane juice. Dere are two long pieces of wood wid a horse attached to dem. Someone push de cane between de rollers. De horse gallop round, an de rollers squeeze out de cane juice. Dey call it a sugar mill. De cane juice run through a big tube into three big black pots, which are already on de fire, ready fi catch de cane juice. It boil in de first pot, den run on de trough to de next pot. As de juice run from pot to pot, it get thicker. By de second pot, it is thickening, an is now molasses. When it reach de third pot, it get thicker still, an is what we call 'new sugar'. Dem put de sugar in big pans --kerosine tin -- an it cyan serve for a long time."

All of this is done in the Boiling House with the Sugar Mill. Higglers can sell it in the market, maybe a quart, pint or half pint. They have different size containers to measure the sugar and they set their own price.

But Uncle Zekie seh him get to learn that the making of sugar spread all over Jamaica, Barbados, Antigua and other places in the Caribbean, in those days. But why we need sugar? I ask Uncle Zekie.

"It is part of our daily life, in our food an drink. Some sugar is necessary for de body fi function well, fi energy, an it mek us feel good. We cook an bake wid it, an put it in some dessert."

But as time go by, Uncle Zekie tell me, there was a big improvement in the making of sugar, so we now have better brown sugar, and white or granulated sugar. When we look back over the years, we see that sugar-making in the boiling house was an important part of Jamaican life.

FIVE

Saturday Soup — "Satiday Soup"

According to Uncle Zekie, in Jamaica, the long-time tradition is that every Saturday (Satiday), "everybody a mek soup – all kind a soup. If yuh tek a walk from house to house, yuh surprise fi see de different kine a soup. De rich family a mek soup an de poor man a mek soup too. No matter what kine a soup, an what yuh afford to put in dere, is still soup fi de Satiday dinner, an de family dem -- adult an pickney --enjoy it. Even if de pickney dem no want it, dem have to learn to like it, for is only one pot cook."

"Dere is all kind a soup, according to what yuh afford – beef soup wid de meat from a special part of de cow, soup bone soup, corn pork soup, tripe soup, gungu peas, red peas, black eye peas, ham bone an green bean soup, chicken soup, which is good when yuh have a cold or de flu. Den you can mek a meatless soup wid just de peas or beans, an yuh vegetables. But let wi not forget de pepperpot soup wid callaloo, green corn, even okro sometime, an any kine a vegetable yuh can find."

Uncle Zekie seh that he can't describe to me every kind a soup, so he will confine himself to two kinds – rice peas soup and chicken soup.

"Yuh ever hear bout rice peas soup? Dem call it so because de peas grain dem look like grains a rice – fine an nice an delicate. A lady had a whole heap on her fence, It run like a vine, wid plenty green leaves, an de pods long an hang down. But when de pods turn brown, it ready to use. So she pick dem, shell out de peas, which look brownish, reddish, an use dem for soup. She put plenty in a big iron pot an add pigs tail, corn pork, corn beef or de smoke tripe from de creng creng over de fire. Whatever meat she choose, she put in de pot wid de peas an let it boil. She soak or boil de salt

out a de meat before she use it. Pieces of yellow yam, coco, irish potato, dumplings are put in. She cyaan forget de seasoning – onion, garlic, thyme an pepper. She stir it now an den, an when it tasty enough or come to de right consistency, den it ready – so yuh grab yuh bowl an enjoy.

Chicken soup is done in de same way, but yuh use de wing, leg, back, neck – all de boney parts. De same kind a food is good, but since chicken soup is used sometimes when yuh have de flu or a cold, yuh can leave out de dumpling, yam an so on, an just mek a broth.

Uncle Zekie seh he could tell me how they use to make more kinds a soup, but what him say already is enough. "If yuh want to hear more, wait til next time." But he continues to say that things get better now. There is still Saturday soup, but many people now have the blender, the electric cooker, the crock pot, so we have to move with the times and with new developments.

SIX

Sunday Dinner

Uncle Zekie tell me seh that every family in Jamaica, rich or poor, always like to have a special dinner on a Sunday. "De women dem nuh need no special recipe. Dem just throw in tings and cook, and it always turn out nice. Some a dem can bake – cake, pone[3], even wedding and birthday cake, especially for members of de family and friends."

So, you can imagine what the high class woman that him know do when she prepare for Sunday Dinner. "First, she select a nice pretty table cloth, de plate dem, knife and fork and spoon fi put on de table an mek it look pretty and special. She did belong to de class of people who in dem days have maid to help her. From de day before, dat is, Saturday, she decide what she going to cook. Plenty tings around dat she can choose from – maybe roast beef, roast pork, spare ribs, curry chicken, oxtail and bean, steamed fish, or escoveitched fish, an de list goes on.

Suppose she choose to roast a leg of pork? She buy it in the market – de maid season it up from Saturday, with onion, garlic, thyme, salt, pepper an whatever else she choose. She might add some barbecue sauce. She take a sharp knife, stick holes in de meat, stuff de seasoning in it, put it in a safe place, cover it and leave it until Sunday. Den she put it in a deep covered baking dish, an bake it at 350 degrees. When de leg of pork get soft, she remove the cover, so it can get a brown color. She makes de gravy an place it in a dish for de table.

---

[3] A firm pudding, that cuts like a cake. In Jamaica, chefs make sweet potato or corn meal pone.

Den de maid put de meat on de table. Of course, she is wearing apron an cap. Den she put on rice and peas, macaroni an cheese, a vegetable salad, an whatever else she likes. If she is cooking escoveitched fish, she select it, clean it, season it de day before cooking it. She fry de fish in oil, maybe coconut oil, remove it to a dish. Den she sauté a mixture of onion, garlic, pieces of tomato, carrot, a little vinegar, all in oil an she pour it over de fish, perhaps decorating it wid parsley an anyting else she might choose.

What about de dessert? It might be a piece of cake or pudding baked from Saturday an some juice or even a little wine."

But Uncle Zekie, is this what the rich people used to do in those days? What about the poor family who can hardly make it, --time hard, money scarce?

"Guess what, dem still content yuh know. Dem might have some run dung an salt mackerel over some rice, piece of yam, or wid green banana, or some cook up saltfish wid whatever food dey can find."

But only talk is no good. Tell me how you cook any of those things, for I don't know.

"Yes, to mek rundung, yuh need salt mackerel, coconut milk an seasoning. First of all, yuh buy de mackerel, soak it overnight in cold water, wid a little vinegar or lemon juice. Den yuh get a good dry coconut, grater it, an squeeze out de juice - de coconut milk. Boil de milk in a suitable saucepan an when it turning custard, before it mek oil, add de seasoning an de mackerel, simmer for a while, an yuh run down is ready. Yuh treat de salt fish de same way. Boil it, an when it is not too salty, yuh remove de bones, den cook de seasoning in a little oil, an add de fish. Some people even add a little curry. Yuh can serve dese two dishes wid any food yuh like – yellow yam, rice, sweet potato, plantain, cassava.

De poor man in dose times could feel just as good at Sunday dinner as de rich man. Poor people learn how to be content wid what dem can afford. Contentment an happiness is good for de soul."

SEVEN

Crucifixion Eena de Yard

Uncle Zekie seh that he remembers when people were very self-sufficient in Jamaica. In the country, they grew their own food – fruits, vegetables and ground provisions – and reared their own animals – goals, pigs, chickens and cows. These animals provided meat and sometimes milk for the family. He told me an interesting story about killing the animals, for meat, which he called "Crucifixion eena de yard".

He seh: No cross never put up you know, but some killings did gwaan. De fowl dem might have a chance fi prepare fi de slaughter, but de pig or de goat[4] never have none. A farmer raise fowl, pig, goat an even cow. But him could'n manage fi kill a cow, so him haffi kill goat – sometimes ram goat, pig or fowl.

Nowadays no matter how big and old de fowl is, we call dem chicken. De farmer put dem away in de fowl coop for at least two weeks an give them special food fi eat. But de goat and de pig never have such luck wid special food. Dem had to eat de same ole pig food or grass dem use to get til dem day come, even though dem a go provide meat fi de family and friends – partiality!

To kill a chicken (fowl) him tek a box, put de chicken underneath with de neck outside an one a him foot on de box to keep it firm. Den him cut off de

---

[4] A ram goat is a male goat.

chicken head. You hear it fluttering under de box, and when de sound gone, you know it dead. So, you tek it out, den pick off the feathers, an clean it up." Uncle Zekie seh: "One man mi know no have refrigerator, so him put salt on de chicken an dem call him 'Corn de cock'.

To kill a pig is a different story. Him just catch de pig an cut off de head. When him sure that de pig dead, him cut it open. Him remove de intestines (tripe) an other parts, an hang it up open in a specially prepared place. Someone cleans de intestines, put seasoning on it, an put it in a creng creng[5] over de kitchen fire to smoke it. De rest of de meat dem use in different ways fi de family. Dem no have to buy meat for a while. De pickney dem stand round de meat hanging dere, an dey have fun frying up fresh liver an light[6].

The animals were crucified, but there was no cross. Uncle Zekie seh that he used to love those times when everybody in the family could gather around these tasks, and enjoy each other's company in a nice and humble way.

---

[5] Since there were no refrigerators in the old days, meat was preserved by smoking it. The creng creng was a wire basket hung high over the fire used to smoke the meat.

[6] Another word used in Jamaica for the lungs of the animal.

HOUSEHOLD CHORES

EIGHT

Cleaning the Floor in the House

A Uncle Zekie seh this.

"Is a long time now, but everybody like to keep de place where they live nice an clean an pretty. Yuh no have to be rich to keep yuh house good. Yuh have one little house fi yourself in one little corner in de country. But is yuh pride and joy, so yuh try yuh best to keep it clean and nice. Yuh put up pretty curtain, but most of all, is de floor. When yuh go a Miss Matty house, yuh surprise to see how de floor shine, yuh hardly want step on it. Yuh can see you face when yuh look on de floor, like yuh looking in a mirror.

But in those days, de house dem did small an mek wid board flooring, mostly two rooms. Yuh know many people did have that kind a house, until dem can do better. 'Yuh haffi tan pan crooked an cut straight.'[7] Mr. Freddie an his family is a big example. Him go to a tree call 'logwood'[8] in de community. Him strip off de bark an boil it in a kerosine pan til de water turn red. Den him store de water an use it fi wipe de floor. To clean de floor, yuh just wipe it wid de reddish water an den leave it to dry. Den yuh use de coconut brush an wax de floor wid nuff bees wax til it shine. Sometimes de ladies have fun using de brush. To make de work seem even lighter, dey clean a certain way, down on dem knee singing a little tune.

---

[7] This means: You have to start in a humble way until you can improve.

[8] Logwood is a type of flowering tree native to southern Mexico and Belize that was introduced to the Caribbean in the early 18th century. It is used in traditional medicine, to treat diarrhea and excessive bleeding. A red dye can be extracted from the tree bark, and this was used to color textiles in Europe. The British had a thriving trade from the Caribbean in logwood. In Jamaica and elsewhere in the Caribbean, the dye was used to stain wood floors.

But tings gradually change til they start using tile for flooring in plenty houses. Yuh just wipe de tile wid a mop wid soap, water an a disinfectant. Just leave it to dry an perhaps spray it wid something to mek it shine. Den comes de 'saviour' -- carpet. Yuh no have to do anyting, but it more expensive. Yuh buy a little machine --a vacuum cleaner -- an use it to clean de floor. But yuh can also have a nice pretty board flooring, because some people allergic to carpet. If yuh afford it, yuh can get yuh carpet or board floor clean professional. So yuh see, we really improve."

'Tank de Lawd', according to Uncle Zekie.

NINE

Laundry — Washing Clothes

All of us know that if you wear clothes, sooner or later you have to wash them. But washing clothes in "de good ole days" was very much different from what many people do nowadays, according to Uncle Zekie. For there was no washing machine and dryer, and there was no laundry room in the house. "Dere was a big basket or a big bath pan eena de house an for de week, if yuh tek off a piece of dirty clothes yuh put in deh."

Monday was generally washing day, but the different things to do to the clothes mean that washing could last for a whole week. To begin, you get water from the river or a catchment tank next to the house (if you were lucky), some soap - blue soap, brown soap, whichever you choose (no soap flakes[9] yet). If you need a brush, you could use a corn stick. To make a corn stick, you roast the corn on the cob and after you eat the corn the corn stick is left. That is what you use. You could also use a scrubbing board.

Uncle Zekie described the process: "First yuh separate de white clothes from de colored ones. Yuh handwash de white clothes. Yuh put three stones wid wood in between an mek a fire. On de fire yuh put a kerosine pan wid water. After yuh soap an rub de clothes properly, yuh put them in de pan, especially de white clothes, an keep turning dem wid a clean piece of stick which yuh keep for this purpose. Yuh can also use a clean piece of zinc on de ground nearby, put de soaped white clothes on it in de sun, an

---

[9] Laundry detergent

keep damping it wid clear water. Yuh den wash an rinse de colored clothes in de meantime, an put dem out to dry. Yuh have a clothes line in de yard. Dere are two posts plant securely in de ground several feet apart an a long piece of wire stretch out an tied securely to each post. De post is generally wooden an very strong to bear de weight of de wet clothes. De clothes are pinned wid clothes pins onto de wire, so dey get de heat of de sun an de breeze passing trough. On de second day (Tuesday), yuh rinse de white clothes – two rinses an now yuh ready for de white clothes to dry.

When de clothes get dry, it is ironing time. Yuh damp de clothes by sprinkling a little water on each piece. Den yuh roll dem up an put dem in a zinc bath pan. Yuh make up a wood fire an put a few "sad irons"[10] to heat. To use de iron so that yuh don't get burn, yuh hold it wid a cloth pad. Den to clean de iron face, you rub it on de ground in some ashes an on a banana leaf, an den it ready to use. Yuh amazed to know dat it iron de white shirts as clean as ever – no soiling. But dere is another kine a iron called de "tailor iron".[11] Yuh light some coal an put it in de iron, for it have a space fi hold it. Den you cover it an hold de handle an iron de clothes. But white clothes an colored clothes get ironing on different days."

This all you do to keep your clothes clean, long, long time ago. A so Uncle Zekie seh.

---

[10] A sad iron is a small iron – all metal, with a small handle, that you heat on the coal pot or on a wood fire.

[11] A tailor iron Is a larger iron used by tailors in old time Jamaica.

SELF-CARE

TEN

Taking Care of Yourself

Uncle Zekie tell me that his mother used to tell him and force him to eat certain things, even if he didn't like it, for she used to say, "Yuh are wha yuh eat", and if you don't eat good food, you get run down, and you have to run to the doctor often and pay plenty money.

Speaking of doctor, he seh that "nobody like to go to de doctor, except if him a yuh special friend. As dem see de white coat, dem get anxious an wonder what de doctor going seh. Dem call it 'White Coat Syndrome.' Sometimes is being anxious for nuttin. It is like yuh try fi step over a wall, an when yuh lif up yuh foot high to go over, yuh find out that dere is no wall at all."

Uncle Zekie seh that once his daughter was sick and so he called the doctor. "In dose days, doctor come carrying him briefcase. Him open it an tek out a thermometer, an a stethoscope. Him look in her eyes, her ears, an tek her blood pressure. But him mek one mistake. Him looking at her teeth an tongue, she push out her tongue an him tek him finger holding it down to look in her throat, an she just bite him finger. But him was very good, because him put two white tablets on her tongue, an in a short time she felt better."

Every two weeks, the medical officer would have a clinic in the cross-roads. He would bring a container with a liquid medicine, and everybody with their different illnesses would leave with a little bottle of that medicine. But it did help some of them. One doctor said that everything he gave this woman, she complained that it did not help her. He was so tired of her that he mix up something in a little water, so it taste sweet. "She tek it and come back an say: 'Praise de Lord, a feel good now.' So she could tell everybody in de community how good a doctor him was."

Uncle Zekie seh that taking care of your body is very necessary. One thing you have to do is to bathe or shower regularly. He remember that long ago, only the wealthy folks could afford to have a bathtub or shower in their homes. The poor country folks used a bath pan with water. Sometimes they would put the bath pan of water in the sun, and bathe in it when it was warm. His mother would rub up cerassee bush in the water to keep his skin clean and smooth. The body lotion was homemade coconut oil. His mother used Ponds Vanishing Cream for her face and Ponds Cold Cream for her body. You could bathe outside if you wanted, or you could take the pan of water inside.

But what about the dentist, I asked, because so many old people are going around "toothless." They cannot afford to get a denture or a "plate."[12] Uncle Zekie seh that for his age him have good teeth, for after each meal him brush him teeth with toothbrush and toothpaste or he use chew stick. He seh you have to be careful to go to a good dentist, because his uncle did go to one who put him to sit in a chair, and he use a kind a instrument like a pliers to pull the teeth.

"It pain him so much, dat him rail outa de seat an jump so high, him nearly touch de ceiling. Him never have so much pain from him bawn. What hurt him most was de dentist seh to him, 'Come on, dat is not anyting!' "

Uncle Zekie's Auntie Tim would always say, "A woman hair is her crownin glory," and she take good care of her daughter's hair from she was a little girl. She would put aloe vera juice or Seville orange juice in it before washing it with soap. Then she rinse it properly and towel dry it, then leave it for fresh air to go through it. Then she put black castor oil in it, and make it into beautiful plaits.

---

[12] The colloquial name in Jamaica for false teeth.

The men and boys wash their hair when they shower or bathe. There were no recognized barber shops in the community, so this man took his son to a man in the area who cuts hair in his house. His son did not like it because the man blew on him to remove the hair from off his shoulder. The man said his wife would trim his hair and shave him, and also do the boys hair, so they started a barber shop at home.

Uncle Zekie seh, "yuh can be creative an have fun with yuh family in yuh own house. Dat is your lesson for today!"

ELEVEN
The Pit Toilet (Latrine)

"Lawd a massi! Yuh neva hear bout dis -- de pit toilet?" -- Uncle Zekie asked me. "Well, yuh know dat before sewage come in, no toilet was in de house dem time. It was outside. Dem dig a big hole, a pit dem call it, an it must be square. Dat is why dem call it "pit toilet". Den dem fit a little square house on it. De house must fit even an good over de pit. It must cover over de edge a de pit, right over it, so dat dere is no space for air to get under it. De toilet is a little building outside not far from de main house, so dat when yuh feel de desire to go, yuh don't have too far to walk. Some people call it de 'small house'."

The toilet had flooring like any other house, but inside was different. There were two seats raised from the floor. One was higher than the other. The lower seat was for children and the higher one for adults. Each seat had a board cover fitting closely. Some pit toilets were nicely kept.

"Dem use to wipe de floor wid dye made from logwood tree bark . It was red and them shine it wid a coconut brush an bees wax. Yuh tek de dry coconut, an cut off one end of it without touching de coconut shell inside. Den yuh have de brush. Dere was disinfectant too, mainly liquid jeyes[13] which yuh threw onto de toilet seat after use. When yuh use de toilet, be sure to cover de seat well. De toilet never have any light inside, an when yuh go dere, if is night or night soon come down, yuh have to carry yuh

---

[13] Jeyes is a liquid disinfectant used widely long ago in Jamaica.

lamp. But yuh can't carry yuh nice 'Home Sweet Home' lamp[14]. Yuh have to make yuh own lamp. Dis is where creativity come in handy. Yuh mek a bottle lamp. Yuh tek a bottle, a small neck bottle like a drinks (soda) bottle, pour some kerosene oil in it. Roll up some paper to fit de bottle mouth. Put it tightly in de bottle, lean it over to let de oil soak in de paper and light it wid a match stick. Den yuh have yuh lamp."

Apparently his friend Miss Sara complained that her pit toilet was too near the burial ground – the cemetery --and she was very afraid to go to the toilet in the dark.

"She afraid of de duppy dem. So she ask her bredda to go wid her. Him was good yuh know, for him would a stand up outside de toilet an wait til she finish what she was doing -- always holding de bottle lamp. Den him escort her back to de house."

What a good brother!

But how Uncle Zekie know about everything so? He seh that telling these stories is a wonderful way to appreciate life in those days, when people made use of what they had.

---

[14] This is an oil lamp called the Home Sweet Home lamp because these were the words printed on the glass base of the lamp The base held kerosene oil, and it had a gold-colored cap, with a cotton wick, and the height could be adjusted with a small winder attached to the cap. Clamps on the cap held the glass lamp shade in place. See https://jamaica-gleaner.com/article/art-leisure/20171126/celebration-jamaicas-heritage.

CHURCH

TWELVE
Going to Church

Uncle Zekie Seh:

"All over de world from long time ago, from 'Adam was a bwoy', people going to church, but since mi never born yet, mi can't tell yuh about any of these foreign places. In my country, mi see people go a church from mi was a little pickney, when mi eye dey a mi knee. Mi hear seh some people did come in as slaves from Africa. But after some time Missis Queen set dem free. Dem settle down in some little village, but dem was still singing an dancing de African way. Dem shout an clap an sing an pray an preach. Sometimes, de Church was a hut wid coconut branches, leaves an other shrubs. De floor was dirt, an mi nuh sure if dere was any seat. Dey might shake tings fi mek music.

As time went on, dey start to mek a church or de meeting house made of board wid board flooring. Den de next thing, dey learn to build a church out of cut stones join together wid concrete. Dey get so sophisticated now dat dey begin to mek church wid nuff style. Different kind a church startup, Church of England (Anglican), Baptist, Church of God, Holiness, an de list go on."

A Baptist church was in my community. They had benches (pews). Sometimes a large family can occupy an entire pew on Sundays. Uncle Zekie seh him was born a Baptist, and to become a real serious Baptist, you have to get baptized. They took him and some other persons to a big pond nearby and dipped them in the water.

"Yuh haffi stan up wid yuh arms folded to yuh chest, an hold yuh breath, an Parson dip you in de water an take yuh up quick, quick. Friends surround yuh an sing hymns. Yuh haffi carry clean clothes to change in a booth dat dey build not far away. So all yuh sins now wash away an yuh is filled wid de Holy Spirit. On de next Sunday, yuh dress go to church, tek communion an get receive as a member of de church.

One man used to come to de church in a buggy drawn by a horse. Him wife use to cover her foot wid a nice pretty, shiny piece of cloth. Him wear three piece suit an she wear hat an gloves. Den him escort her from de buggy into de church, an when church over, put her back in de buggy. One woman, always dressed nice an proper, come to church late every Sunday. But she always carry a fan, an when she come in, she sit in de front bench a look on Parson, an where Parson can see her. Den she start fi fan, from her foot up to her face."

According to him, "de church did have a belfry, dere dey keep de bell. De floor of de belfry was a flat square made of concrete. De four post of concrete slant a little an reach up to de top, where de bell is hanging wid a long rope tie on to it. De bell ringer pull de rope an de bell ring. De bell was useful, because dey ring it to make people know dat it is was time for church, dat a church member dead, dat something important happen, or a calamity like a storm."

So this is the church, which holds a valuable place in the community.

THIRTEEN

Harvest Festival at the Church

First of all, Uncle Zekie seh that his parents used to take all them children to the Baptist Church every Sunday. But he remember when they used to have a big celebration starting on a Saturday and lasting sometimes until the Monday of the next week. It was something that they planned to make some money for the church. But the members of the church had to prepare for it for a very long time.

It was called Harvest Festival. Church members would cultivate various things in the garden for a whole year. They saved them and warned everybody – "don't touch those things, they are for harvest."

He tell me that his father would plant yam, coco, dasheen and potato, and at harvest time he would call his friends to help him with the reaping. Sometimes he even pay somebody to help him. He was a small farmer you know. They dig up the big tall yam, careful not to cut it with the machete. Then there were also fruits and vegetables, lettuce, carrot, tomato, the big sweet grapefruit, orange, soursop, tangerine, Jew plum and guinep. Don't forget the tall white and red striped sugar cane.

The ladies would decorate the church and make it look beautiful. They would bring hand embroidery, crochet, all kinds of things, even aprons and caps, dresses for little girls, pants for little boys, hats and caps. They would also bring cakes, puddings, biscuits, and all kinds of food -- curried goat, ackee and salt fish, fried dumplings, rice and peas, home made juices.
All this preparation was done before Harvest Sunday. The choir would rehearse to sing, and everybody would come to church. The choir would lead the congregation and sing hymns like this:

"Come ye thankful people come
Raise a song of harvest home
All is safely gathered in
E'er the winter storm begin
God our maker doth provide
All our wants to be supplied
Come to God's own temple come
Raise a song of harvest home."

The Pastor would preach a sermon about giving thanks. The Harvest celebration was a very serious and solemn affair, an occasion when people give back to God some of what he has given them and thank him for his many blessings. A collection offering would be taken.

On the following Monday, there would be a sale at the church. People from the church and community attended and made purchases. Many people would just come with their family to relax and have a delicious meal. Special people were responsible for selling items and collecting the money, which went to the church to be used for some special purpose. It was a very relaxing time for some folks. They met people that they hadn't seen for a long time. They might ask one another riddles, play games, do puzzles, give jokes, tell stories, or even try to do some artwork, drawing things they saw around them.

These were not the days of the computer, or the iPhone, and that is all that Uncle Zekie seh about Harvest Festival.

HAVING FUN

FOURTEEN

At the Beach

Uncle Zekie seh that since Jamaica have so much sea around it, going to the beach, especially on a Saturday or Sunday, was a favourite pastime, because people can relax after they work hard for a whole week. Let me tell you all that him seh. He know lots of things, like the many beaches in Jamaica – Bournmouth, Wickie Wackie. But the one he like best was Gunboat. Then you have the one in Ocho Rios, - Dunn's River Falls - where the river water runs into the sea. But the boss one of all, according to him -- Negril Beach -- is "de best," because he live near to it. The sand is white and the water clear and clean as crystal.

Uncle Zekie tell me that when people going to the beach, they have to dress a certain way. Him sey:

"Tings change now, but de woman use to wear bath suit – two piece, and brazzierre on top, an all de bottom cover up, only de middle yuh could see dem skin – de midriff – an push-in-toe sandals.[15] Yuh could see them legs, some pretty, some not. Den some a dem go beach fi show off demselves, wid de makeup an hairdo. Dem nuh really want to bathe, or to wash off dem makeup. But if dem bathe, dey wear bath cap. Dem flirt round fi mek other people see dem, especially de man dem. Better still, dem sometimes oil dem body wid a mixture of coconut oil, olive oil an drop little perfume in deh, so dat when dem pass yuh, dem smell sweet."

Uncle Zekie seh that the men dress differently.

---

[15] Now called Flip Flops.

"Dem topless, so yuh can see dem muscles, de hair on dem chest. Covering de bottom, dem wear a ting yuh call (bath trunk). It mek like shorts, but it is far above de knee. He don't know why dey call it Bath Trunk, for him madda had a ting dey call trunk, an she put clothes or anything special in dere. Dey swim an dive so dat everybody can see dem. But when dem walk round, yuh can see dem foot good -- but dem wear sandals or walk barefooted.

At de beach, some men tek dem family, especially if it is a special celebration like a birthday. Den dey walk up an down arm in arm wid their wife. Some beach have a house, wid bed, shower, kitchen table, seats, everyting, so when yuh come outa de sea yuh can relax. Some people go to de beach just to be wid dem friends an enjoy de cool sea breeze. Dey carry food an drink an sometimes music, so dat dey can ketch a little dance in a different place. Considering everyting, de beach is good fi de body, for de warm sea water help get rid of some of de aches an pains dat people have."

So Uncle Zekie seh him encouraging everybody to go to the beach when they can, even if you have to travel far. Get in the car, or take a bus, and go every now and then, for if you don't, "yuh missing someting special."

FIFTEEN

When School Nuh Keep

Uncle Zekie seh that he grew up in a big family. He had two brothers and two sisters. All of them had to go to school, but they had their special chores to do every morning. He had to make sure that he got up early enough to milk the goat or the cow to get milk to put in his father's coffee, for he always liked his special milk in it.

But him seh dat: "On certain days, like Empire Day, no school keep. On dose days children free fi have picnic, fi party, eat up all kind a food an have a jolly good time wid their family." The day he liked best was a rainy day when he couldn't go to school. You see, in the country where he lived, rain fell so heavy sometimes that it was safer to stay home.

Let me tell you what him seh about the rain.

"Sometime it very heavy, an yuh can hear it falling on de zinc roof, an yuh can even see hailstone a drop outside. Also dere can be breeze an yuh see de trees dem bend over, like when yuh have a hurricane. Water full up de road, an full up yuh shoes, for although him parents poor, de children never go to school barefooted."

Him seh what he liked best about the rainy day was the food.

"We get nice drinks like aerated water, things we never get to drink except on a rainy day. Mi madda would make a big pot a soup - chicken soup -- an I use to like de yellow yam and coco an dumpling in it, especially de dumpling. Everybody got their bowl a soup. When we finish eating an wi belly full, we want to sleep, so mi sister dem get a chance to cover-up in de four poster bed an me an mi brodder dem lie down underneath. Everybody a sleep. Mi daddy a sleep an snore on de sofa in de living room, but mi madda awake an cover over wid umbrella an gone to de kitchen outside to wash de dishes an tidy de place. When she come back inside, she get fi her sleep in de chair (if she can).

When all we pickney wake up, we can get some bulla an pear, or toto, lemonade, coconut drops, an mi daddy get coffee tea. Mi madda usually drink someting too. Guess what we do now? Mi sister dem tek out dem doll, comb de hair, dress dem up an start sew dolly clothes. By de end of de day, all de dolls dress up in new outfit. But we boys only sit down or stand up an watch dem. If we have space we play ring games. We boys can jump over one another, ask riddles, or mek a sketch of something, but mostly we like to watch wi sisters. Mi Madda might come in an start to sew, but mi daddy feel dat him must entertain everybody, so him lie down on de couch, have everybody round him, an keep them happy an laughing by telling them all kine a jokes."

So Uncle Zekie seh he used to be glad and happy when school nuh keep.

SIXTEEN

The Moon

Why should anyone think of the moon? It is one of the wonders of the world. Uncle Zekie seh that the moon is very mysterious, and he's not sure, but he thinks that anywhere you go in the world you can see the moon. You can see the moon in the daytime, but mostly at night.

The moon is round, way high up in the sky, and if the sky is blue, you can see it better. Sometimes it looks like a man in it holding a bundle of sticks over his shoulder. It can take different shapes. Uncle Zekie seh that his father could look at the shape of the moon and tell you whether it was going to rain, whether there would be a drought, or whether they were going to have hot or cool weather. It could also tell him when to plant his crops.

Him seh that: "In dose days gone by, some people neva have clock in de house, an dey depend on de shape of de moon, to guess de time. One early morning mi daddy was going to town, an was depending on de moon, but when him tink it was near daylight it was just after midnight. No cock neva crow an him spend de greater part of de night at de cross roads waiting on de bus. Also, mi daddy tell mi dat dey have certain people who do a ting dem call astrology. Dat is de study of de moon, an other heavenly bodies, like de sun an stars, an how it affect yuh fortune. As one of dem who do de astrology was mi good friend, me learn tings from him."

Uncle Zekie talks about those days when there was no electric light, and so besides the moon, people depended on lamps or lanterns. There was the "Home Sweet Home" lamp. The bottom of the lamp was a container with a wick. You would put in kerosine oil and the wick would get soaked in the oil. The lamp had a lamp shade or chimney made of glass and on it were the words: "Home Sweet Home". You would take off the lamp shade, turn up the wick and light it with a match. Then you would replace the shade. But you had to keep the shade clean and keep it shine and sparkling. So now there would be light in the house, so you could read, study or do what interest you.

Uncle Zekie seh that the most interesting thing to him though was the moonlight – they call it 'moonlight night'. At certain times, the moon was large and shining bright up in the sky. Sometimes the neighbour's children would come over to his yard, and they would play games, hop scotch, Hoola Hoop, Jacks, Skipping, for the girls. They sometimes played a game called 'Little Sally Water'. Boys and girls would be in the ring and they would choose a girl sitting in the middle. Her name is Sally Water. Then they would sing:

Little Sally Water
Sitting on a saucer
Rise Sally Rise
And wipe your eyes
Sally, turn to the East
Sally, turn to the West
And chose the one you love the best

The girl, representing Sally, would do all the actions. She would choose a partner, perhaps a boy. They would clap and sing and dance around in the ring, and Sally would take them back to his or her place. Skipping is another game they would play. When they skip the fastest for the longest time without stopping, this they call 'Pepper'.

The boys sometimes would join the girls, but their favorite game was cricket – 'Bat and Ball'. They would use a coconut bat and a small orange or a Seville orange for the ball. They had wickets made of sticks and also wicket keepers, bowlers and batsmen. This was much fun on a moonlight night.

Their parents would sit and enjoy the fun. His mother would provide refreshment for them, such as banana dumpling and salt fish, and many other things too good to mention here. So, the moon and the moonlight night was very much appreciated by Uncle Zekie and his family in the good old days.

CELEBRATIONS

SEVENTEEN
Empire Day

Uncle Zekie tell me about Empire Day and how Jamaicans celebrate it. I ask him why Empire Day? Because the first thing that come to my mind is what they mean by Empire? I think he seh that he agree with me that an empire is a number of countries under one ruler, a king or queen.

"Dere was talk about de British Empire when Queen Victoria or de Queen Elizabeth dem did rule over an control nuff countries all over de world, including Jamaica an other places in de Caribbean. Dose countries use de British flag – red, white an blue – a red an white cross, wid a red an white "x" behind, wid a blue background. Dey call it de 'Union Jack' ".

He continued to tell me that Jamaica and other countries were part of de British Empire. Under the British Empire, a white man from England – the Colonial Secretary - controlled everything – Government, Education, Church. The Church was the Anglican Church, also called the Church of England. Blacks and whites in Jamaica were separated. The white people in Jamaica could even buy them own seat in the church. Black people had to sit down in their own section.

Uncle Zekie seh that: "Queen Victoria did born on de 24th day of May, so all de school dem have to celebrate Empire Day on dat date. School still keep, but dey did not have classes. It was a fun day. De pickney dem dress up in nice fancy clothes. Some of dem can hardly walk because dem shoes too tight, or too big or de heel too high. De girl dem might have red, white an blue ribbon in dem hair. Dere was a big red, white an blue British flag on display. De teachers put it in a central place where everybody could see it, an each child had a little flag to wave. All de children gather around in a position where dey can see de flag. Dey salute de flag an sing:

God save our gracious queen
Long live our noble queen
God save the queen
Send her victorious
Happy and glorious
Long to reign over us
God save the queen"

The rest of the day was fun. The children played all kinds of games. Some took off their shoes. The girls played Basketball, Skipping, Rounders, Jacks, while the boys played Bat and Ball (Cricket), Marbles. At the end of the day, each child was given a bun and some lemonade. They all had a wonderful and exciting day. Some people from the community came to get some of the refreshment.

Uncle Zekie seh, in those days, people did a lot of horse and donkey riding and the bicycle was getting popular. One Empire day in his community, a teacher man wanted to show off how he can ride. "Him saddle up the horse, an sit down in the back. The horse gallop an fling him off. Him lucky that him was not hurt, an him get up smiling and say, 'Oonu see what man can do?' Anyway, one teacher rush in an give him some lemonade."

But Uncle Zekie seh people were glad that they could celebrate and have a good time. That was Empire Day!

EIGHTEEN

Independence with a Vengeance

Heaven help us! Uncle Zekie seh he don't know where they get those words – Independance with a Vengeance -- from, for he was born a long time ago and he never heard that before. A tell you he is a bright man and he knows everything. He says the correct word is "Independence". Jamaica became independent on August 6th 1962. This is what he told me and he is right. He also seh that he thinks the word vengeance described the vigour, liveliness and fun that did accompany that celebration.

He is teaching me, but maybe he doesn't know that I learnt all these things about independence in school. Uncle Zekie seh: "when yuh become independent, yuh on yuh own. Yuh can manage yuh own affairs, like when pickney leave dem parents' yard an gone live in dem own place."

He explained that Jamaica and some other countries in the Caribbean became independent in the 1960s – Jamaica, in 1962. No longer were they part of the British Empire. Now Jamaica would govern itself. There was a new native black Governor-General, Prime Minister and no-more English man in charge. Jamaica now had its own army, the Coat of Arms, the National Flag – green, black and gold, its own National Anthem and National Emblems, civil service, and judiciary.

Jamaica "High Up" now, important, for the country now became a member of the United Nations. Jamaica is now a real nation, with its own Parliament. But Uncle Zekie, you telling me all this, but what did they do on Independence Day?

"Let mi tell yuh.

Queen Elizabeth, send her sister Princess Margaret wid de message to declare Jamaica independent. Everybody gather at de National Stadium, an it was well decorated in Black, Green an Gold. Alexander Bustamante, who was de first Prime Minister, go wid de Princess to de stadium and dere de British flag was lowered an de Jamaican flag raise up in its place. Dey sing de new Jamaican national anthem wid everybody standing. De stadium did pack up an den dere was entertainment by de school children - singing an dancing. Eating was an important part a de celebration, especially de Jamaica National Dish – ackee an saltfish. To prolong de celebration, dere was street dancing. Special musical instruments did place in different locations like Cross Roads in Kingston, and in de country parts, so people could come an dance in de streets without any violence – peaceful enjoyment.

Uncle Zekie seh that there are other things he has to explain, but he will do that next time.

So, that is how they celebrated Independence in 1962. Thank you Uncle Zekie!

FOLKLORE

NINTEEN

About Spirit

Uncle Zekie seh that when he hears about Spirit he thinks about three things: the Holy Spirit, Duppy (Ghost), or alcoholic drinks. Well, since he is a churchman, he should know about the Holy Spirit and should have it in his life.

"All de church members dem or all a we should have de Holy Spirit to guide us. But some a de Christians dem get possessed, an begin to speak in tongues, an try to heal an prophesy."

In mi community, dere was a shop an on de outside was a sign: 'Get Your Spirits Here.' Plenty men used to go dere, especially on a Friday night, an drink strong alcoholic drinks, like rum, whiskey an beer. Den dem get drunk an talk foolish tings. Him seh all dem try, dem could not prevent a bredda from going dere. One night, him come home an dey smell drink (liquor) on him, an guess what him do. Him nuh tek off him clothes, start whistling, an singing an den take up him bible an seh him a go a church. All him pickney dem run, for dey never see naked man yet. Another time him start to talk Spanish, an at de breakfast table, him look on him wife an seh: 'Yuh face nuh look good. Mek mi fix it up fi yuh.' So, him take de cornmeal porridge an plaster it over her face an seh: 'Now yuh look good. Have dis dance wid mi, or mek we go to Miss Lize party.' Him step forward to hug her an de cornmeal porridge get on him face too. Dem seh him did have a hangover, an if dem did squeeze little lemon juice in him eye, him woulda come to himself quick, quick."

Then Uncle Zekie seh, believe me, there is another kind of spirit. They call them duppy. His grandfather seh that he could see them. When somebody in the area died, they would say that the spirit is always moving around for about thirty days before it disappear. One night the boys were outside playing. All of a sudden they ran inside breathless, and seh "duppy a fling stone." Guess what, it was the neighbour picking breadfruit. Then his sister seh she saw her cousin duppy when she was coming home. It was a banana tree and the way the leaf was hanging, in the dark it looked like a person.
So what about the rolling calf? I asked Uncle Zekie, and he described it like this. It was black, about the size of a dog or pig, with the eyes bright and shiny and rolling around in the head.

"Mi bredda seh when him see dem at night, him have five corn grain in him han, him fling way one, leaving four, an when de rolling calf start looking for it, him run away quick. Also, yuh should know dat if yuh point yuh finger on a grave, it will rotten an yuh lose it. But if yuh see a duppy an yuh mek de sign of de cross, him cyaan trouble you.

Mi cousin seh dat him Aunt Flossie did dead an dey bury her in de church yard, because she did belong to de church. Him sister, a very mischievous person, seh she going frighten dem when coming from Prayer Meeting. So she get one big white sheet, an when dem leaving, she stand up at de gate an cover herself from head to toe wid a big white sheet. When dem come out in de night an see it, dey all run round shouting: 'Mi never know that Aunt Flossie would a show herself to we.' All this ting about duppy is popular superstition."

What do you think?

TWENTY

Anansi

Uncle Zekie seh that from he was going to school he heard about Anansi. They used to call him Brer Anansi and tell the children stories about him. So he wondered who is Anansi? His father should know because he talked a lot to people who should know about such things. He told him that Anansi came from West Africa. A very clever man he is, and so he hid himself in the ship carrying the slaves. When they reached the Caribbean he came off in Jamaica. Anansi is funny and mysterious. They talk about him as a man and he is supposed to have a son called Tacoma. Nobody knows if he was married, but if he was, in West Africa, men could have many wives, and so Tacoma's mother must be the chief one.

But we don't know what to believe, because they say that Anansi is really a spider, but it is confusing, in that sometimes he is a person. He seems to be everywhere and he is dishonest, a liar, deceitful, selfish, not to be trusted, thinks only about himself, and whatever he can get. When he is a man, he says he has certain friends, Brer Tiger, Brer Rabbit, Brer Dog, Brer Rat, Brer Puss, Bredda Ram Goat etc. Notice that although he behaves like a man, his spider qualities make him select animals for his friends because it is easier for him to get along with them and perfect for his very mischievous and skillful nature. He is mean. He spins a little a web, where he lives and which can be seen everywhere, especially in dark corners. Some time ago, in Jamaica, the teachers said they should not be teaching about Anansi in the schools or telling children Anansi stories. They think that the children will learn and imitate Anansi's bad behaviour and that is not good for them. There was plenty discussion about it, but one teacher said: "Nuh ban Anansi, for if yuh ban Anansi, yuh wi haffi ban Miss Lou an Mass Ran.[17]"

---

[17] Louise Bennett-Coverely and Ranny Williams were two outstanding Jamaican comedians in the pre-and post independence period.

Uncle Zekie told me these Anansi stories:

"One day Anansi seh to Brer Tiger: 'Mek we go for a swim in de sea. De water is very warm. Tiger seh: 'Mi cyaan swim so good, yuh know, but mi wi come.' Anansi seh: 'Mi a swimming champion, mi wi help yuh.' So dey jump in de sea. When dey reach far in de nice blue water, Anansi seh to Tiger: 'Mek wi turn over an go in de nice clear water over dere.' As Tiger try fi turn, Anansi jump on him back, an jump off an gone. Poor Tiger just tek him time an swim back to de shore. Anansi already gone hide in him web in de kitchen corner.

Another time, Anansi seh to Brer Rabbit: 'How yuh have so much grass an mi can't get none fi feed mi pet cow calf in this dry weather?' Dey seh 'rabbit nuh drink water an him peepee, an fowl drink water an him nuh peepeee.' You should try fi drink some water. Mek wi swap. Yuh tek this bottle a water an try fi drink it. When Brer Rabbit open him mouth wide an a try fi drink de water, Brer Anansi grab up all de grass an run wid it fi feed him cow calf. Poor rabbit nuh know what fi do wid himself. Anansi feed him cow calf an lie dung a relax in him web in a corner under de table in de cow shed.

One day Anansi invited his friends to come an have a meal wid him. After dey come in de house, Anansi an his friend were busy preparing, table setting, etc. But dey were all talking an dey dress up in fancy clothes for de occasion. Brer Tiger have on a red waistcoat, 3-piece suit, Brer Rabbit, patent sandals; Brer Dog have on Christmas hat; Brer Rat have one lizard round him neck; Brer Puss wid a blue satin bandeau round him head; an Bredda Ram Goat in a black vest. Everybody start talking together an so Anansi seh they better sing. But when dem start fi sing, tings get worse. So Anansi send all of dem into de nearest room. Guess what Anansi do. He go around an put plenty pepper in all de food, so dem cyaan eat it. Him seh to himself, I will wash it off an keep it to serve mi for a long time." So him give him friend dem only some lemonade to make dem satisfy. Everybody was so disappointed an angry. When dem looking for Anansi, him gone an siddung in him web on de house top, a look down on dem an laugh."

Uncle Zekie seh that his father told him plenty more about Anansi, but according to him: "Not everything good fi talk, an yuh have to be careful what come out yuh mouth. Don't be like Miss Mauta Massi.[18]"

---

[18] Mauta Massi is the name given to a chatterbox.

GLOSSARY

An	and	Seh	say; says
Bawn	born	Siddung	sit down
Bredda	brother	Tank	Thank
Bwoy	boy	Tek	take
Cyan	can	Tings	things
Cyaan	cannot	Tink	think
Dat	that	Yah	here
De	the	Yuh	you; your
Deh	there	Wi	our; will
Dere	there	Wid	with
Dese	these		
Fi	for; to		
Fling	throw		
Haffi	have to		
Kine	type		
Lawd	Lord		
Madda	mother		
Mi	I; me; my		
Mek	make		
Neva	never		
Nuh	do not		
Oonu	You (plural)		
Peepee	urinate		
Pickney	child :children		

ACKNOWLEDGEMENTS

If a task is just begun
Never leave it til its done
Be the labor great or small
Do it well, or not at all."
(Anonymous)

I am grateful for the inspiration and the perseverance to bring to you a few stories about early Jamaican life, and to make this book a reality. Special thanks and appreciation to vocal Uncle Zekie, whose pleasure it is to tell stories about his Jamaican experience. I used the information I received from him and worked patiently and diligently to complete the manuscript. Thanks to my daughter, Dr. Winsome Leslie, who worked tirelessly typing the material, editing the manuscript, making contact for illustrations and layout, and for her many suggestions for improvements. To my other daughter, Dr. Heather Leslie-Brown, a deep sense of gratitude for her interest shown in this project and for her many valuable suggestions, enriching the content. To my friend, Mrs. Althea Serrant, for her encouragement and her confidence that the production of this book would be a success.

Finally, thanks to my illustrator Rachel Moss (www.rachelmossillustration.com/) for providing such delightful illustrations to enhance each chapter of the book as well as the cover, making the book more meaningful and interesting. Much appreciation also to Anna-Kaye Wade, for an excellent job on the layout.

Made in the USA
Columbia, SC
23 September 2024

42765943R00041